The Bushmen and Their Stories

☙The Bushmen and

Their Stories

BY ELIZABETH S. HELFMAN
drawings by Richard Cuffari

The Seabury Press · New York

✐ Acknowledgments

I WISH to thank the following publishers and authors for permission to use copyrighted material from the titles listed:

William Morrow and Co., Inc. and The Hogarth Press, Ltd., for the 16 lines of verse on page 21, from *The Heart of the Hunter*, by Laurens van der Post.
Routledge and Kegan Paul, Ltd., and Humanities Press, Inc., for the 3 lines of verse on page 45, from *The Khoisan People of South Africa*, by Isaac Schapera.
Howard B. Timmins, for a quotation on page 121, from *Hunters of the Desert Land*, by P. J. Schoeman.

for Harry
with love

Contents

Alphabetical List of Stories

1 ✒ The Bushmen of the Kalahari

IN THE KALAHARI DESERT of southwestern Africa live people called Bushmen, the oldest inhabitants of all the southern part of Africa.

There are stretches of barren sand in the desert where these people live, but there are also large areas of yellow desert grass and creeping plants, bushes, and even a few trees. In these places, as everywhere in the desert, the soil is sandy and rain seldom falls.

The Bushmen are little people, rarely more than five feet tall. They are slight of build, with long slender arms and wonderfully small hands and feet. People who knew the Bushmen in southern Africa in earlier times said that once you had seen their small neat footprints in the sand you would never forget them.

There are no people just like the Bushmen anywhere else in the world. Bushman faces are often heart-shaped, and their eyes have an oriental slant. In fact, except for their tightly curled black hair, Bushmen are very like the Asian peoples. Their skin color is yellow, though the dust of the desert and the blazing sun darkens it to a copper brown. It is a strangely loose skin and after a number of years it becomes deeply creased and wrinkled. When Bushmen laugh, as they often do, the skin on their faces breaks into countless little folds. People who know them say that the Bushman has a skin like that because it will stretch, so he can eat great amounts of food when he has been successful in the hunt. He must store reserves of food if he is to survive; there is no knowing when he will eat so well again.

The Bushmen are a graceful people. When they walk along, or simply bend to pick up something from the ground, their motions are like part of a dance. They travel across the desert single file, often at an easy trot, and their feet bounce lightly off the ground. The men can run like the wind, fast and long.

Bushmen dress themselves in the skins of animals. A man wears only a leather loincloth and a woman a small leather apron and a big cape called a kaross, usually with a belt at the waist. The cape forms a pouch in back where a baby can ride. The women make white beads of ostrich eggshells and fasten them to tufts of their hair. They string the beads, too, in tiny bands around their arms and knees. Bushman feet are usually bare, but sometimes they wear leather sandals.

Above all, the Bushmen are hunters. They do not grow

food in the earth or herd cattle, sheep, or goats. The men kill wild animals for food with bows and poisoned arrows. Their prey is the eland, a reddish-colored antelope with long horns twisted in a spiral; the gemsbok, an antelope with striped sides; the springbok, a gazelle that springs up into the air when it is frightened. And there are lions, giraffes, and smaller animals.

The women dig edible roots and bulbs from the ground and gather the melons and berries that grow in the desert. Anything that can be eaten must be used as food in such a dry place. Even insects may be a treat. The Bushmen consider ants' eggs a delicacy; they call them "Bushman rice."

The best treat of all is honey, the only sweet food the Bushmen can find in the desert. Eating honey, they believe, brings wisdom.

People who live by hunting move from one place to another in their search for game. The Bushmen roam in small bands that rarely number more than twenty people, most of them related to one another. Home is wherever a family

of "home"—they contain its supply of water. Each one has been filled through a hole cut in the shell and the hole has been plugged with grass. Water can be carried also in a bag made of a gemsbok's stomach.

The Bushmen are among the most primitive people living in the world today. Some people believe that primitive people must somehow be inferior. But this is not the true meaning of the word "primitive." It comes from a Latin word meaning "first." The first people in the world were primitives. Their way of life was earthy and uncomfortable, compared with ours, but these people were by no means stupid and bungling. It took considerable intelligence for man, unprotected as he was, to survive in those dangerous times.

Like primitive people anywhere, the Bushman has an extraordinary feeling of belonging to the natural world around him. He knows every tree and shrub, every hill, and every "pan" in the desert where he can find water. He has an intimate relationship with the birds and the animals, and even with the insects that live on the land. Though he is a successful hunter, he kills only to live, never for the sake of killing.

One Bushman had this to say about the feelings of his people on hunting a springbok: "We have a sensation in our feet as we feel the rustling of the feet of the springbok in the bushes. . . . We have a sensation in our heads when we are about to chop the springbok's horns. We have a sensation in our faces on account of the blackness of the

14

sets up camp, for a few nights or a few weeks—as long as food and water last. Shelters, which the Bushmen call *scherms*, are quickly built of branches and grass. You could stand right beside a scherm and not know it from a bush.

Sometimes no shelter is built at all. Home may be a branch stuck into the sand with the few family possessions hung on it and a place hollowed out for each person to sleep. Nearby is a carefully placed row of ostrich eggshells, often decorated with carved designs—zigzags, diamonds, or pictures of animals. These eggshells are an essential part

stripe on the face of the springbok. We feel a sensation in our eyes on account of the black mark in the eyes of the springbok."

The Bushmen have not always lived in the desert. There was a time when these intrepid hunters roamed over almost all of southern Africa. Since earliest times this had been their land, and they moved lightly over it, knowing they belonged to the land, as the land belonged to them. They hunted on the wide grassy velds, climbed the high mountains, and made their homes in hidden caves or under overhanging rocks.

Much of this was a lush country with plentiful game, flowing streams, and springs of sweet water. There, on the rocky sides of mountains, and in caves, the Bushmen celebrated the land by carving and painting. Many of their paintings remain today. They are of surpassing beauty. Troops of animals, each one painted with loving care, cross the rocks. Huge red birds in formation soar across the ceilings of caves. Slim figures of Bushmen are pictured at the hunt or triumphantly bringing home an animal for a feast. The very stones were worshiped and adorned because they were a part of the earth the Bushmen knew and loved.

For the Bushmen all this is changed now. They are gone from the rocks and caves where once they painted. There are no Bushman painters anymore. Centuries ago, no one knows just when, yellow-skinned and black people invaded the Bushman land from the north. They despised the little hunters. Ruthlessly they pushed them back, massacring almost every one they could find as they took over much of their most fertile land.

Later, white people, many of them of Dutch descent (called Boers), invaded the Bushman land from the south, pushing north and east. They had come from Europe to settle on the southern tip of Africa and now they wanted fresh land where they could farm and raise cattle. These people considered the Bushmen of the desert "wild," and they slaughtered them like animals. Now and then, instead, they would capture some of them and keep them to work on their farms. These Bushmen, and those who came to live on the fringes of civilization, were called "tame" by the whites.

The Bushmen knew their own worth. Though they are normally peaceful people, they fought fiercely for their land and for their lives. They stole or butchered or hamstrung the enemy's cattle and sheep. To the very last they remained proud and defiant, unwilling to accept the white man's ways. They were smaller than all the invaders—black, yellow, and white. They were vastly outnumbered by the black and yellow-skinned people who overran them. The Europeans were not so numerous, but they had guns that outshot the Bushman's arrows, and horses that ran faster than he could.

When they had been hunted down and slaughtered beyond endurance the Bushmen retreated to the desert, to live there in peace on land no one else wanted.

16

Whether he is alone or with others of his family group, the moon and the stars, the rain and the wind are the Bushman's companions. His knowledge of these things is not just that of a hunter and food gatherer who must depend on them in order to survive. He knows them as a part of his daily life and as a living part of the world through which he moves. He has a feeling of being known to these things, too—of being, himself, a necessary part of this world.

This feeling of belonging is, after all, a feeling of love.

To the Bushman, everything in the world was made by spirits who are everywhere around him, unseen, and who still watch over the world. This is the religion of the Bushmen, and they tell about it in their stories. They tell, too, of the creation of the first Bushman and of the doings of the people of "the early race." Whatever they tell comes to them from within because, as one Bushman said, "always there is a dream dreaming us." And they believe in the meaning of this dream.

The Bushmen have woven into their stories their feelings about themselves and the natural world around them. These stories have been told by the old men to the younger people for countless years. Thus they have passed from generation to generation, changing in the telling, but always keeping the Bushman's feeling of wonder at whatever is mysterious and unknown in the world outside and within himself. From these stories the Bushmen themselves learn, time after time, about their own place in the great design of life, from its beginnings long ago on into the present and beyond.

There are several groups of Bushmen in the desert. Not all of them tell the same stories. They do not all hold exactly the same religious beliefs, though they share their understanding of the world around them and their feeling of wonder at their place in it. Most of the stories in this book come from Bushmen who lived in the southern part of the Kalahari.

A Bushman who was away from his companions in the desert missed, most of all, his stories. These meant home to him. Without his story a Bushman felt that he had nowhere in the world where he could feel sure he belonged.

One Bushman, named "Dream," was put in jail because when he was hungry he had killed a springbok for food on land that had once belonged to his people. While serving his sentence he told a sympathetic white man: "I sit waiting for the moon to turn back for me, that I may return to my place, that I may listen to all the people's stories. . . . I must only await the moon, that I may tell my master that I feel this is the time when I should sit among my fellow men. I must first sit a little, cooling my arms, that the fatigue may go out of them. Then I merely listen, watching for a story . . . that it may float into my ear, while I feel that a story is the wind."

There are those in Africa who have said that the Bushmen are among the greatest storytellers of all time. In this book you can read some of their stories and something of how the Bushmen have felt about them.

2 ✒ Rain

Water is the most urgent problem of all for the Bushmen in the Kalahari. The dry season is long, and in the midst of it, in June and July, there is winter. (Below the equator winter comes when we have our summer.) Nights are cold then. Water left standing in an ostrich eggshell freezes. Grass is touched with frost. An icy wind blows all night long. During the day the sun warms the desert, however, and life for the Bushmen goes on as usual.

After the winter there is the long hot season during which everyone longs for the rain that does not fall. Animals are hard to find; they have gone away to search for water. Few birds fly. The Kalahari in this season has been called "The Great Thirstland."

Hunger and thirst depress the people, but they have known such seasons before, and most of them will survive. They know how to find water in this desert. There is water in the tsama melons that grow there. It can be gotten out by making a hole in the top of a melon, mashing the inside with a stick, and drinking the good juice. There is even water in some of the grasses. And there are the "sip wells," places where water collects during the rainy season and sinks into the ground. A Bushman can get water from under the earth at a sip well by sucking it up through a straw. It is hard work, sucking up water this way, but water must be had.

There is a Bushman song for the dry season just before the rains. A woman sings:

Under the sun
The earth is dry,
By the fire
Alone I cry.
All day long
The earth cries
For the rain to come.
All night my heart cries
For my hunter to come
And take me away.

And the man, hearing her song, softly answers:

Oh! Listen to the wind,
You woman there;
The time is coming,
The rain is near.
Listen to your heart,
Your hunter is here.

Rain does come at last to the Kalahari. It falls during just three months of the year, beginning in November or December.

The first sign that rain is coming to the desert is lightning that flashes far away on the horizon. To the Bushmen this is the most welcome light of the year. All the living creatures in the desert have waited for this light through the long dry season, with desperate longing. Once the lightning appears, even though not one drop of rain has yet fallen, animals follow after it in thousands, from one end of the vast wasteland to the other. Bushmen set out for the West, too. Even a promise of plenty of food and water on the spot will not stop them.

Lightning, however, is also something to be feared. It can strike a person and even kill. Bushmen are taught from childhood to look straight at the lightning without blinking. If they do this, they believe, the thunderbolts will turn away from them, frightened of wide bright eyes that shine like themselves.

Often the rain comes fast. A sudden wind whirls dust into the air with a roaring sound. The lightning that has hovered on the far horizon rips across the sky. Loud thunder follows. Then cascades of water drop straight out of the sky. Rivers run down the sides of trees. Water rushes down stream beds that have been baked dry for months under the hot sun. All the earth is drenched.

The Bushmen huddle in their huts as the rain falls. Young girls hide themselves completely under their capes.

If the lightning sees them, they believe, it will strike them and turn them into stars or into flowers that grow in the water.

Sometimes, though, the rain comes gently, blowing across the land like a mist. The Bushmen say there is no scent as sweet as that of this rain.

After the rain the desert bursts into bloom—white blossoms along the branches of the few trees, gay flowers of many colors on the dunes, all growing from seeds that have waited in the hot dry sand. The flowers bud, blossom, and bear their seeds quickly, for the season is short.

The Bushmen feel that new life comes to them, too, when the rain falls and the earth grows green.

Rain, say the Bushmen, was once a person of the early race. That is, he was a person long ago, in earliest times. In those days animals, too, were persons, and Rain could take the form of any animal he chose.

RAIN AND THE YOUNG WOMAN

IN THE FORM of a bull Rain once visited a young woman, to court her. Down to earth he came, trotting through a mist that was made by his own breath. He scented the

23

fragrance of the woman and followed it until he found her. She saw him coming and wondered who this could be. But she must have liked what she saw, for she threw a bunch of fragrant herbs on the head of the Rain Bull. Gently she picked up her child, laid him down on her cape, and covered him. "Sleep, sleep," she said, "I must go."

Then the woman climbed up onto the back of the Rain and together they trotted along, trotted along. She watched the trees as they went, and she grew tired. After a time she said to the Rain, "You must go to that tree in the ravine just ahead and set me down, for I ache."

The Rain stopped by the tree and set her down. She rubbed him all over with fragrant herbs she had brought and after a while he went to sleep.

The woman stole quietly away and went home while the Rain slept under the tree. She rubbed herself to take away the scent of the bull, until all that remained was the sweet smell of the rain.

Finally the Rain felt cool under the tree and woke up. He thought the woman was still on his back and he trotted away to a spring where clear water bubbled up out of the ground. That was where he belonged; from water he could make life-giving rain for the people on earth. And now he could do it better because for a little while the woman of the earth had been with him, she and her sweet-smelling herbs.

Perhaps when the Bushmen women sing the Rain Song, asking for "my hunter to come and take me away," they remember this tale of the Rain's visit to earth so long ago.

Other Bushmen tell a different story about the Rain. These are Bushmen who have known the villages where white people or black people live. They speak of houses, and doors that can be fastened.

◢ THE CHILDREN OF RAIN

IN THIS STORY Rain was a beautiful woman who lived long ago where the sky grows rosy before the sunrise. She wore a rainbow about her waist.

Rain married the man who created the world, and they had three daughters. When the eldest was grown up she decided to visit the people on earth.

Rain said, "When you go to the earth you will find good people and bad people. Beware of the bad ones."

The daughter went to the earth, fell in love, and married there. So from that time on she lived among the people of the earth.

In time her mother in the sky had a fourth child, a boy named Son-eib. The eldest sister on earth did not know about this son.

Years passed. The two younger girls missed their sister.

One day they said to their mother, "We would like to visit our sister on earth."

Son-eib wanted to go, too. But Rain was afraid to let all her children go. "You might get lost," she said.

Wolf was then living in the sky. He heard what the mother said and he approached her. "I will go with your daughters and your son and show them the way," he said. "I know the earth people."

The mother was still afraid, but her husband said, "Let them go. Tomorrow you will have another child."

So they all set out together.

But Wolf had evil plans. The two daughters were beautiful and he wanted them for himself. He planned to get their brother out of the way.

As they traveled along, Son-eib could feel that something was wrong. He was worried. When Wolf and his sisters were not looking he caught a pretty red bird and hid it under his belt.

They walked for a long time, many days and many nights. Finally they came to a large village where good and bad people lived. A woman approached. She looked Son-eib up and down. "This boy's eyebrows are so like my mother's," she said. "How can this be?"

Wolf was annoyed. "Don't pay any attention to him," he said. "He is not a human being, he's just a thing. We don't even give him food."

Son-eib was very angry when he heard this, but he said nothing. When the villagers brought food for the travelers, Son-eib did not eat.

Towards evening the same woman came again and said, "This boy has my mother's eyebrows. Let him sleep in my house."

Wolf was angry, and he shouted, "You don't know what you are talking about! He is just a thing. He must sleep in a hut by himself."

There were bad people in the village who listened to Wolf. They shut Son-eib up in a hut outside the village and fastened the door on the outside.

At last it was dark. The woman and all the other good people of the village were asleep. Wolf and the bad people crept up to the hut where Son-eib was sleeping and set it on fire. Tall flames rose to the sky. Son-eib perished in the flames. But a beautiful red bird rose up from the flames and flew through the clouds.

The bird flew to where Rain lived and sat in a tree beside her. "Son-eib's sister did not know him," the bird sang. "Son-eib is dead. He perished in the fire."

Rain called to her husband, "Come and hear what the bird has to tell!"

He came and he listened. "What shall we do?" he asked.

Rain was angry. "Why ask *me* what to do? Your name is Fire! I am only Rain." And they walked away from each other.

A little later a small cloud came floating through the sky. It moved towards the village where Son-eib had died in the fire. Around the cloud was a rainbow. It grew bigger and bigger.

The people in the village were very much afraid when they saw this. They ran towards their huts. But there was no use in hiding. Out of the rainbow fire flashed down to earth. This was a special fire from the sky and it killed only Wolf and the bad people.

The rainbow then stretched wide over the earth, and a mighty voice was heard coming from the sky: "Do not kill the children of the sky!"

Ever since that time, these Bushmen say, people have been afraid of the rainbow. When they see it in the sky they take two pieces of wood, strike them together and shout: "Go away! Do not burn me! Go away!"

3 ✒ Stars

NIGHT COMES SWIFTLY AND QUIETLY in the desert, and then the vast dark sky overhead is bright with millions of stars. To the Bushmen the night is far from silent. They look up at the night sky until they themselves feel a part of it, and in the quietness they hear, coming to them from everywhere above them, the murmuring of the stars. It is like a faraway sound of the sea.

The stars, say the Bushmen, are great hunters. Some are greater hunters than others. The brightest star in the Great Dipper hunts in dangerous places in the shape of a lion. Its eye shines bright and fierce in the sky and its roar can be heard on earth as a distant murmur.

When the stars are very busy hunting you can hear their hunting cries: "Tssik! Tsah!"

The Bushmen say the stars have heart in plenty. A Bushman mother will ask the stars to take the heart of her baby

32

boy and give him, instead, some of their own, that he may have the heart of a hunter. She asks this as a prayer, holding her child high above her head towards the night sky.

To the Bushman the stars are not faraway gleams from other worlds. He speaks of them as members of his family. The two most brilliant stars in the South African sky are "Grandmother Canopus" and "Grandmother Sirius." The Bushman's spirit and the stars converse with one another.

Bushmen say that the bright star Sirius is so big it must possess food. They pray to her: "Give me the heart of a star, that I may not hunger."

They light the end of a piece of wood in the fire and raise it up towards Grandmother Sirius, moving it up and down quickly like a bright torch. They rejoice; they sing to both Grandmother Sirius and Grandmother Canopus. Here are the words of one such song:

Sirius!
Sirius!
Winks like
Canopus!

Canopus
Winks like
Sirius!

Canopus
Winks like
Sirius!

Sirius
Winks like
Canopus!

The torch and the singing, say the Bushmen, will help both Sirius and Canopus to shine warmly in the sky.

Grandmother Canopus is the "Bushman rice" star. Canopus especially can send food. When Canopus first shines in the sky it is time for the Bushmen to go looking for ants' eggs. The Bushman prays to Canopus:

O Star coming there,
Let me see a springbok,
O Star coming there,
Let me dig out ants' food . . .
O Star coming there,
I give you my heart,
Do you give me your heart . . .
Let me eat filling my body,
That I may lie and sleep at night.

The Bushmen believe that many of the stars were once people of the early race, long ago before there were any Bushmen on earth. Here is a story about the stars in those early times.

✒ THE ASHES OF THE MILKY WAY

THERE WAS ONCE a girl of the early race who felt great loneliness because she was by herself in a hut. None of her family or friends were with her. She felt she must do something—anything—to ease her loneliness. So she put her hand into the wood ashes of the fire and threw them into the sky, telling them to "lie white along the sky." These ashes became the Milky Way. Because of its light, for the first time people could see their way as they returned home late at night.

The Milky Way gently glowed, say the Bushmen, because it felt that it was wood ashes. And the girl who put this little light in the sky felt less lonely because this was something that had meaning for all the world. There would not be even a little light on moonless nights if the Milky Way were not there—it and the other stars.

Then there is the story of Dawn's Heart, called by us the morning star. According to the Bushmen, Dawn's Heart is the greatest of all the star hunters in the sky. Long ago he was a person of the early race. As a person he came down to earth, fell in love with Lynx, and married her. (She, too, was a person at that time.)

Today, as then, Lynx is a lovely creature, brave and full of life, moving with vivid grace through the grass and bush and forests of Africa. A suitable spouse for a star.

35

The villain of this story, on the other hand, is the hyena, which comes out of its hole only after darkness has fallen. The hyena is strong, yet it has a reputation for being a coward. Its wail in the night is a weird wild sound that sends fear into the heart.

⌐ DAWN'S HEART

ONE DAY Dawn's Heart was away hunting, leaving Lynx at home with her child. The Hyena saw this and she prepared to bewitch Lynx. She took perspiration from her armpits and mixed it with the food Lynx was about to eat.

Now food to primitive people is never just food. They believe that whatever a person eats he will become. A Bushman father will give his son the heart of a leopard to eat, because no animal is braver than the leopard and eating his heart will make the child brave.

When Lynx ate food that contained perspiration from the Hyena's armpit, she was doomed. The armpit is a very special place; from it comes the particular spirit of a man or an animal that makes him what he is. The she Hyena had turned Lynx's food into concentrated hyena spirit, and this was evil.

36

At once, after eating the food, Lynx's earrings fell off, then her bracelets and anklets. Her cloak made of animal skin loosened and fell down, and her skin petticoat. The thongs that tied her sandals broke and her sandals slipped away. She was naked. Screaming, she ran to hide among the reeds that grew beside the water. She had lost the things she needed for her life on earth. As the Bushmen say, she felt as if her thinking strings would fall down, and if that happened, she would die.

Meanwhile the Hyena put on all of Lynx's pretty ornaments—her cloak, her petticoat, and her sandals. She walked proudly about.

Lynx's younger sister came to help. The baby cried with hunger and the sister begged the mother to come out of the reeds and nurse him. She did come—once, twice, three times—saying, "I am here!" but the spell of the Hyena grew stronger and finally Lynx could not feed her child at all. It was not that she did not want to feed him. She felt herself slipping away from everything that had been real to her—the world she had known, Dawn's Heart, her sister; even her child. Little by little she was forgetting that they had ever been.

Meanwhile Dawn's Heart had come home, not knowing anything was wrong, and was in his hut. Pretending she was Lynx, the Hyena entered the hut. In her evil way she wanted to destroy not just Lynx but Dawn's Heart as well. The star's light would then be turned to darkness.

But the sister of Lynx rushed into the hut and told

37

Dawn's Heart that this was the Hyena and that the Hyena's plans were dark and evil.

Dawn's Heart leaped into action. He grasped his spear and hurled it at the Hyena. He missed. The Hyena was not even scratched. Darkness and evil cannot, after all, be done away with entirely. The Hyena was frightened, however. She ran away so fast that her feet were burned in the fire outside the hut. She would never again be quite so dangerous in her evil. The Bushmen say that because the Hyena burned her feet in this way all hyenas are compelled even to this day to slink home at dawn with a limping gait, as if their feet hurt.

Lynx came out of the reeds and nursed her baby. Then she put on her petticoat that the Hyena had left behind,

her cloak and sandals, and all her pretty ornaments. Now she remembered. This was her world and these were her people.

All this was long ago. Dawn's Heart is now a star in the sky; he does not walk the earth. But he has not forgotten how near he and his bride came to disaster. He is watchful as he comes into the morning sky; his bright eyes flash with light and the animals that roam in the night turn and run to their holes. Dawn's Heart carries a spear ready, in case the Hyena has been up to her tricks, and he drives it into the earth as he strides along.

The Bushmen see Dawn's Heart in the sky and feel safe. As long as he is there, surely the evil powers of darkness cannot do them harm.

4 ✍ Moon and Sun

For countless years the Bushmen have watched the moon grow smaller in the sky, night after night. And when it seemed that it might disappear entirely they have rejoiced to see it grow bigger, little by little, until its full brightness lit the darkness of night for men.

The Bushmen do not know the scientific explanation for this changing moon. They know only how it looks to them and how they feel as they watch its changing shape. They have their own story to explain this.

42

🐦 *THE RIVALRY OF SUN AND MOON*

WHEN THE bright full Moon shines in the night, the Sun sees him and grows angry. This Sun is a kind of fiery god, bringing warmth and light to the earth in the daytime. He does not want the Moon to shine so brightly in the night. He follows the Moon, to chase him away. But the Moon stays right where he is. So the Sun cuts pieces off the Moon with his sharp rays, little by little, and the Moon grows smaller and smaller. The Moon does not want to die. He begs, "Oh, Sun, do not destroy me entirely! Let me keep my backbone for the children."

The Sun takes pity on the Moon and leaves his backbone alone. But the Moon is badly hurt; he goes away to hide his pain. Then he appears again as a thin new Moon and grows and grows, wandering in the night, until he is a full Moon once more, lighting the dark. Again the Sun is angry. Again he follows the Moon and cuts off pieces, little by little. . . .

When the moon is full the Bushmen sing and dance all night around their fires, to show the moon that they love its light and want it to come back to the night sky after its light has faded. If they did not do this, the Bushmen believe, the moon might change entirely and never return. Hour after hour under the full moon the rhythmical songs continue, like the waves of the ocean. Hour after hour there

43

is the rhythmic stamping of feet on the ground, followed by the pattering sound of feet moving fast and lightly.

The medicine man then howls to the moon and with a scream runs across the fire. In a trance, he falls unconscious on the ground. Thus he is drawn away from his everyday life on earth. He has made contact with the spirit of the moon.

The rhythm of the night-long dance, and the singing, is the rhythm of life itself. The sun, the stars, and the moon are all a part of this rhythm. The dance is a way of acting this out, of repeating the rhythm of the universe so that it will never fail.

Let the small moon grow big again, let the night sky be bright with stars, and when night is finished let the great sun rise, bringing the day.

The new moon is important to the Bushmen in a different way. With his right hand raised a Bushman prays to the new moon for food:

> *Ho, my hand is this,*
> *I shoot a springbok with my hand*
> *By an arrow. . . .*

> *Ho, Moon lying there,*
> *Let me kill a springbok*
> *Tomorrow. . . .*
> *Let me shoot a springbok*
> *With this arrow.*

44

Let me eat a springbok,
Let me eat filling my body. . . .

Ho, Moon lying there,
I dig out ants' food
Tomorrow,
Let me eat it. . . .

Ho, Moon lying there
Look now at this arrow
That I may shoot a springbok with it tomorrow.

When drought has laid waste the land and the desert seems almost too dry a place for people to survive, Bushmen may dance to the new moon and sing a prayer that asks for rain:

New Moon, come out, give water to us
New Moon, thunder down water on us,
New Moon, shake down water for us.

The Bushmen say that their god Mantis created the moon. How he did this is part of a story later on in this book.

A story about the Moon and the Hare tells of death, which to the Bushmen is still another part of the timeless rhythm of life.

45

✒ THE MOON AND THE HARE

LONG AGO, when the Tortoise was a person of the early race, the Moon sent him to the people on earth with this message: "As I die and return again, so shall men die and return again."

The Tortoise started off to deliver the message. He repeated it over and over again to himself so he would not forget it. But he was so slow on the way that he forgot the message in spite of himself. He turned back to ask the Moon to tell him again.

When the Moon heard that the Tortoise had forgotten the message he was very angry. He pushed him aside and called the Hare, who was then also a person of the early race. The Moon said to the Hare, "You are a swift runner. Take this message to the people on earth: 'As I die and return again, so shall men die and return again.' "

The Hare ran off quickly, but soon he found some green plants to eat, so he stopped and grazed. He stayed so long that he, too, forgot the Moon's message. But he was afraid to go back and tell this to the Moon. So he tried to remember and when he thought he had the message right he continued his journey. But he got it all mixed up. He told the people on earth: "The Moon says that, unlike itself, you will die and not return again."

46

When the Moon found out that the Hare had made such a terrible mistake he was more angry than ever. He beat the Hare on the mouth and split his lip. Ever since that time the Hare has had a split lip.

When the Bushmen see a hare they remember the message of the Moon. The Moon had said that death was not meant to be the end of life, and the Hare who told otherwise bears the mark of his punishment forever.

All day, every day throughout the dry season in the Kalahari the hot sun bakes the desert to dry leaves and dust. The twisted branches of leafless trees are outlined against the hot cloudless sky as if someone had etched them there. The sand reflects the sun's rays and all the air shudders and dances with a rhythm of its own.

The Bushmen say that the sun makes a ringing sound in the sky. As long as a Bushman can hear this sound, he feels that all is well; the sun-within-himself has not lost contact with the great light in the sky that brings life to the world. It is a harsh world in the dry desert, for the sun can bring thirst and death. But without this sun there would be no world at all. Each morning the sun rises to light up all things for men. Under it men walk about, go hunting, and return home.

Sometimes a Bushman feels faint as he returns home under the hot sun. Then he throws up into the air a handful of earth. The people at home who are waiting for his return see the dust and know that he needs help. "The sun is killing him," they say. "It is his heart. We must quickly go to give him water." And they run to him, carrying cool water.

There is a Bushman story about the sun and how it came to be in the sky.

⚓ THE SUN MAN

THE SUN was once a man, but not of the early race; he lived as a man at the time of the first Bushmen who inhabited the earth. A great light shone from the Sun's armpits. When he raised his arms it was day and when he lowered them it was night.

In time, however, the Sun Man grew old and slept a great deal. There was darkness not only at night but during the day. People were cold. They felt they could not live this way. "We must throw the Sun Man up into the air," they said. "Then we can get warm again all over, and his armpits will shine and bring daylight to us."

An old woman said to the children, "Go to the place where the Sun Man is sleeping. Go carefully, grasp him firmly, and throw the old man up into the air."

The children did as they were told. They approached the Sun Man slowly, making no more sound than a man does when he hunts a springbok. They stood still in the darkness and looked at the Sun Man as well as they could, making sure they knew where to take hold of him. Carefully they all put their hands under the Sun Man's shoulders and legs, and he felt hot.

Then, all together, the children lifted the Sun Man up and threw him high into the air, saying, "Oh, Sun! You must go up into the air. You must shine there and make the whole earth light. You must make heat for us, so we will no longer be cold."

After they had done this the children went back home to their people. Shining high in the sky, the Sun became round, and it never was a man again. Ever since that time the Sun has been warm and bright in the sky, like fire.

When the sun's light comes to the earth, people can see each other; they can see the meat they are eating. They can visit together and talk of this and that in the sunlight.

When the sun sets, darkness comes, and it is time then for the stars.

5 ✒ Wind

THE BUSHMEN SAY THE WIND was once a person of the early race. He was a child. When the Wind-Child stood up the air was still and everything around him was calm. When he lay down the wind began to blow and things moved about. When he started kicking his legs as he lay on the ground the huts people had built blew away and vanished in the distance. Bushes bent and broke in the wind. So much dust swirled through the air that people could not see. There was no knowing when the Wind-Child would kick his legs and all this would start happening.

It was a frightening time. No one knows what might have happened if the Wind-Child had not had a mother who came and put him on his feet, and a father who built a hut to shelter him. Wind was a young thing with all of life ahead of him, and he needed the love and care of his father and his mother. Without that he could have destroyed too much of the world and the people in it.

Later Wind became a bird and lived in a cave in a mountain. He no longer walked about; instead, he flew. When he was hungry he would come out of his cave to look for food. When he had eaten he would return to his cave.

A man could make a mistake about this Wind-Bird. More than once a Bushman has thrown a stone at a bird, only to discover that it was the Wind. Angry Wind would blow fiercely then, the grasses would bend down, and the air would be full of dust. This would go on until at last Wind went home to his cave in the mountain.

The Bushman felt the wind inside of himself as well as without. His breath was the wind. When he died his own wind went to join the greater wind without, and together they made the clouds that send rain.

Before the wind could make clouds with a man's breath, however, it would blow over the ground, making swirls of dust to erase the footprints that showed where the man had walked about when he was still alive. When his footprints were gone from the sands everyone would know that the man was dead; it was important that they should know.

A man could make clouds while he was alive, too, but he did not do this with his breath. On a hot day he would sit in the shade watching a cloud growing bigger and bigger in the sky. He felt that his liver had left him to help with the making of this cloud.

The great clouds billowing up in the blue sky before a storm were "a person's clouds." People had helped to make them; some when they died, some while they were still alive.

When he thought about the clouds in the sky the Bushman felt lifted out of himself. He felt that all the people and all the spirits of the sky and the earth belonged together. They would be remembered forever as a part of the invisible world people feel around them and inside themselves.

He felt this even as he went about the daily business of living—fashioning his poisoned arrows, stalking an animal on the hunt, carrying it home for his clan to eat. The women felt it as they dug for roots and gathered the juicy melons of the desert, as they cared for their children and made beads of ostrich eggshells.

The wind played an important part, too, in the story of the ostrich feather that grew into a big ostrich.

✒ THE OSTRICH FEATHER

A BUSHMAN killed an ostrich and carried it home. Some of the ostrich's feathers were bloody and the Bushman's wife put them on nearby bushes to dry. Then the Bushman and his wife settled down to a meal of ostrich meat.

While they were eating, a little whirlwind came along and blew on the ostrich feathers. One little feather with blood on it was carried up into the sky, where it whirled around. Then it fell down out of the sky into the water, where it became wet. And suddenly it was no longer just an ostrich feather. It came alive as it lay in the water. It became ostrich flesh; feathers grew on it, and wings. Legs grew while it lay there and the new little ostrich walked out of the water and basked in the sun at the water's edge. All its feathers were black, because it was a little male ostrich.

When his feathers were dry the ostrich walked away from the water, unstiffening his legs and strengthening his feet. He lay down to rest while his breastbone became bone. Then he walked again and ate small young plants, because he was only a little ostrich. And he roared, hardening his ribs so they, too, would become bone.

The little ostrich let himself grow. His flesh became stronger and he felt heavy because his legs were big, and his knees. He grew great strong feathers. Now he could roar strongly, for his ribs were big.

He was a grown-up ostrich with long wing feathers. He went home to where the big ostrich had been killed when he was one of its little feathers. There his wives laid eggs and he took good care of the eggs, because they were indeed his children.

So the dead ostrich came back to life because one little feather with a drop of blood on it whirled in the wind, dropped into the water, and came alive.

6 ✒ Mantis

THE PRAYING MANTIS IS THE Bushman God. The Bushmen could have chosen something big and impressive, such as an elephant or a lion, or one of the other marvelous creatures of Africa. But instead they chose an insect, small as they are small, with a curious pointed face that suggests a Bushman face. The praying mantis turns his head and gazes ahead with his bright eyes, seeming to contemplate the beginning and end of everything in the world.

The Bushmen know that great things can come from small beginnings. The mantis itself begins as a tiny invisible egg that becomes a worm crawling on the earth before it is transformed into a long-legged creature with wings.

The Bushmen believe that Mantis created all things. He gave them their names and their colors. It is he who sends the welcome rain and brings good hunting to the hunters. He protects the people from illness and danger. Nevertheless, the Bushmen do not worship Mantis. They pray to the moon and the stars and sometimes to the sun, but not to Mantis.

There are many Bushman stories about Mantis. He is a kind of dream Bushman. Though he has supernatural powers, he is very human, too. He is full of mischief and often gets into trouble by playing tricks. There is no malice in Mantis's tricks, however. He is forever trying out different ways of behaving and learning from his mistakes. Most of all he is learning to know himself.

The stories about him deal with an earlier time when many of the animals and birds, and Mantis too, were persons. All these were to become true animals, birds, or insects at a later time. In the stories they seem to be sometimes persons and sometimes animals—or even both. Thus, Blue Crane, who apparently is a girl-person, has a wishbone, like a bird.

Mantis accomplished his wonders through these person-animals. He had his own kind of magic, too. Often in the stories, when disaster is about to descend and it seems as if life itself must fail, Mantis has a dream. The dream tells him what to do, disaster is averted, and life goes on.

Mantis can bring dead persons back to life again, and he does this over and over again. To save himself in moments of great danger, he often gets wings and flies away, usually to the water, an ancient symbol of life, where he can renew himself and make a brave new beginning.

Sometimes, as in other Bushman stories, humble things

are changed to something bright and shining. Ashes become the Milky Way. Mantis makes the moon from an ostrich feather.

Mantis has a large circle of family and friends. His wife is Dassie, the African rock rabbit. She is a practical home-loving person, much like the animal she is to become, and she helps Mantis to keep his feet on the ground. Often she has to get him out of trouble. Mantis and Dassie have several children, among them young Mantis, who is much like his father.

Then there is Mantis's adopted daughter, Porcupine. Her own father is a fearsome creature called the All-Devourer, and because she is afraid of him, Porcupine comes to live with Mantis and his family.

The porcupine is an animal much loved by the Bushmen. She comes out only at night and grazes under the stars on green grass and tender roots, sniffing about with her sensitive nose. Her dark shining eyes show her the way in the dark. Only when the Dawn's Heart strides into the sky does the porcupine return to her deep hole in the ground. As a person in early times Porcupine's life was somewhat different, but at that time, too, she was one who could always find her way.

Porcupine's husband is Kwammang-a, an early person who is not destined to become animal, bird, or insect. He is a part of the rainbow come to earth, and just as the rainbow divides the white light of the sky into its separate colors, so Kwammang-a can understand what is going on

60

around him and divide feelings and thoughts and happenings into their separate parts.

Porcupine and Kwammang-a have two sons: young Kwammang-a, who is brave and quiet like his father, and Mongoose, who is always scolding and pointing out to Mantis what he has done wrong. It is Mongoose who keeps Mantis from getting too great an opinion of himself.

As an animal, the mongoose is a creature of both the sun and the earth. His home is a deep hole in the ground, but he comes out to kill the reptiles and snakes that are his food. When he is not busy with this necessary work he loves to sit in the sun with his fellow mongooses. Mongoose as a person of the early race, like mongoose the animal, was both earthy and sun loving.

These, then, are the persons of Mantis's family. Where did Mantis himself come from? There is more than one Bushman story about this and about the origin of the first Bushman.

⌁ MANTIS COMES ALIVE

ONE STORY tells us that Mantis was present at the very beginning of the world. He was carried by a bee over the dark windy waters that covered the new earth. Bee, the honey-maker, is an image of wisdom. But this was a very tired bee, his wings stiff and cold in the endless night wind. His burden, Mantis, became heavier and heavier.

Bee looked for a bit of solid earth where he could set down this burden. There was no earth. The bee flew slower and slower, nearer and nearer the water. At last, floating on the water he saw a great white flower, half opened, waiting for the morning sun. He laid Mantis to rest in the heart of the white flower and planted within him the seed of the first human being, safe from the wind. Then the bee died, and Mantis came alive in the morning sun. There, too, the first Bushman was born.

⋈ MANTIS AND THE OSTRICH

IT WAS Mantis who brought fire to people. Long ago in the early days people did not know about fire. They had no light at night and all their food was eaten raw.

Mantis noticed, however, that there was always a delicious smell wherever Ostrich was eating. Nobody else, people or animals, had food that smelled so good. One day Mantis crept quietly up while Ostrich was preparing his meal and watched him. Ostrich was roasting his meat on a fire. When he had finished he picked up the fire and carefully tucked it under his wing. Then he walked away.

Mantis decided that he would have to get this fire, but he was certain Ostrich would not give it to him. For days he went about trying to think of some way to trick him. At last he had a plan.

Early one morning he went to see Ostrich. "Ostrich," he said, "I have found a tree with the most delicious yellow plums—just the kind you love. Come with me and we'll eat them."

Ostrich was delighted and followed Mantis into the desert. When they came to the tree Ostrich at once began to eat.

But Mantis said, "Those are not the best plums. The ripest ones are at the top of the tree. Reach higher!"

Ostrich reached higher. Mantis urged him on. "That's not high enough! Look at that ripe one way up there, the grandfather of them all."

Ostrich wanted that high one. He stood on tiptoe, opening his wings to balance himself. At that moment Mantis snatched some of the fire from underneath Ostrich's wing. He took it home and gave it to the Bushmen. After that everyone could have roasted meat and a light in the dark of night.

Ostrich was very much ashamed. He knew he had been tricked. Since that time no ostrich has ever flown; he keeps his wings close to his sides for fear of losing the little fire he has left.

Ostrich, say the Bushmen, was a person in earliest times, and such persons often do extraordinary things. The ostrich always puts one of its eggs outside the nest. All the other eggs, often thirty or more, lie close together in the warm sand, and then there is this one outside.

The Bushmen explain that the ostrich does this because he is still brooding over the fire that was stolen from him by Mantis. This makes him absent-minded, so he and his wife deliberately put one egg outside the nest when they are hatching eggs. Seeing it there, they will be reminded of what they are doing. Otherwise they might forget that they are sitting on eggs and walk away.

Poor ostrich! The Bushmen use the shells of his eggs to store water and make beads for decorating themselves, but they do not hesitate to laugh at him.

More stories of Mantis follow, with bird-persons and animal-persons and the fearsome All-Devourer.

7 ◢ Blue Crane's Story

MANTIS CARED GREATLY FOR many small young beings. One of these was his sister, Blue Crane.

Blue Crane was once a person of the early race. Blue Crane's friend, Frog, and her husband were also persons.

One day Frog's husband was sitting and sulking because his wife would not speak to him. A beetle came flying past his nose and he jumped up and followed it. Blue Crane jumped up, too. She wanted to catch Frog's husband and bring him back. She went along, snatching at him until he disappeared under a flat stone.

Blue Crane did not see where he went. She searched and searched, following Frog's footprints. Then she went back and found her own footprints, and finally she was all mixed up.

"This is where I ran," she said. "I tried to grab my friend's husband here."

She grew sad while she kept on searching, and lean, until she was just bones.

Two lions heard her talking and stole up, following the sound of her voice. They killed her and ate her. As they did so, Blue Crane's wishbone sprang out of the mouth of one of the lions and went and lay nearby. The lions tried to find it, but they could not see it and they went away.

Then Mantis came looking for his little sister. He saw the tracks of the lions, followed them and found the place where they had killed Blue Crane. He went along searching until he saw her wishbone lying there, for it was big. Mantis knew what to do. He picked up the wishbone and put it into the water. Then he went home to his hut.

After a while he came and looked in the water. Blue Crane's wishbone had become Blue Crane! She was standing at the edge of the water and she was very young and little. When she saw Mantis she was frightened. She jumped up and splashed into the water. So he went back to his hut and waited.

After a time Mantis went out again to look. He saw Blue Crane sitting in the sun. She had grown. This time she did not see him and he turned back without startling her. While she sat basking he went to make clothes which he meant to give her when she grew up.

Again he went out, and Blue Crane was still sitting in the sun. She seemed to be a girl. He left her in peace, for he wished her to sit quietly.

Then Mantis took the clothes, because he thought that now Blue Crane had grown up. He went out to where she sat basking and put down the things. He stole up to her and caught hold of her. She struggled, trying to get into the water, but he held her fast and rubbed her face with his perspiration so she could smell his scent. He told Blue Crane that he was her elder brother Mantis. She should stop struggling and sit down.

Then Blue Crane sat down. Mantis put a cap he had made on her head and he gave her a cape and a skin apron. She put on the cape and tied on the apron.

Blue Crane went gladly with her brother, Mantis, and together they returned home.

8 🖾 The Little Springbok

Mantis was digging wild bees' honey out of a hole and throwing it to his beloved pet, the little Springbok. The little Springbok was sitting on the earth that had been thrown out of the hole, and eating the honey.

While Mantis was digging, some elephants came along. The Mother Elephant picked up the little Springbok, put it on her back, and walked away. She left her own Elephant Calf sitting by the hole where Mantis was digging.

Mantis threw some honey out of the hole and said, "Are you eating, as I am eating?"

The little Springbok did not answer.

Mantis said, "What is the matter with the child? Why does it not speak to me when I ask it whether it is eating?"

He cast out more honey and said again, "Are you eating, as I am eating?"

Then the Elephant Calf said, "Kurru!"

And Mantis said, "Listen! What is the matter? What

can have happened to the child's throat, to make it answer me like this? I cannot understand what it says. I will throw out more honey and listen again."

So Mantis threw out more honey. "Are you eating, as I am eating?"

The Elephant Calf said, "Kurru!"

Then Mantis got out of the hole and looked. He found the Elephant Calf sitting covered up with earth.

Mantis said, "This person must have been sitting here. That is why I called without an answer."

He brushed the dirt off the Elephant Calf and sent it away.

When the Elephant Calf had gone, Mantis wondered how it came to be sitting there. He looked around and saw the tracks of a troop of elephants. He said, "These terrible elephants must have taken the little Springbok away from me."

He turned back, took a quiver with arrows and started along the elephants' track. But then he said, "I must go home first and tell my sister, the little Springbok's mother, about the child. Otherwise she will wonder why we do not come home."

He went home and told his sister, "The elephants must have taken the child from me while I was in the hole."

His sister was angry. She said, "Could you not hear all those elephants when they stood above you?"

Mantis answered, "I really did not hear, for I was digging in the hole."

His sister said, "You must have been asleep in that hole. That was why you did not hear the elephants. I demand that you go and bring back my child."

Mantis asked her to pack some meat for him. Then he would go and look for the child.

"Watch the wind in the grass," he said. "It will blow the grass away from home as long as I am going that way. When I am returning it will blow the grass towards home."

The wind blowing the grass towards home would be an east wind, coming from the place where the sun brings new life to the earth each day. It would tell the sister that Mantis was on his way home with the child.

Mantis then went away and found the elephants' tracks again. He followed them. On a hill he saw the elephants'

huts, and there, playing with the elephants' children, was the little Springbok.

Mantis rejoiced. "My Kattau, my pet," he said.

The elephants caught sight of Mantis as he came over the hill, and the Mother Elephant rushed out of her hut. She picked up the little Springbok and swallowed it. Then she sat down to wait for Mantis. Mantis came up to her and asked her for the little Springbok.

"I have not got it," the Mother Elephant said.

Mantis answered, "You have got it. I saw it playing among the children and I saw you pick it up and swallow it. I have come to take the little Springbok home to its mother."

"How are you going to get it?" the Mother Elephant asked.

Mantis said, "I will get into your mouth."

"I will spit you out."

"I will get in under your fingernail."

"I will pick you out."

While they sat there talking the other elephants closed

in. Mantis stopped talking. He knew how to get into the
Mother Elephant. He went right through her navel, the
place that gave her life before she was born, and on inside
her. While he was doing this the other elephants stabbed at
him with their spears.

Inside the Mother Elephant, Mantis found the little
Springbok and slung it on his back in a skin. The other elephants were waiting to stab him to death as he came out the
same way he went in. But Mantis, instead, came out at her
trunk, carrying the little Springbok on his back. The Mother
Elephant fell down dead.

The other elephants ran all together, closing in on
Mantis again. But Mantis got feathers and flew up and away
with the little Springbok. He called down to the elephants,
"Can you equal me? I am Mantis. I am an enchanter, from
whom you tried to steal this child. None of you can rival
me!"

At home, Mantis's sister looked at the grass. The wind
was blowing it towards home, an east wind.

"Oh, people, look!" she cried. "The wind is where Mantis told me it would be when he was coming home. The
grass is waving. Now it stands quite still, because he is
drawing near."

They saw Mantis as he came carrying the little Springbok,
and the Mother Springbok went rejoicing to meet him. She
unloosed the little Springbok, picked it up and kissed it.
And she rejoiced again.

9 🐭 The Striped Mouse
and the Beetle

This is the story of how Mantis had a dream and the Striped Mouse became a hero.

A long time ago, when the Beetle was a person of the early race, he lived and hunted along a riverbed. The Beetle, as now, was a bustling busybody, always burrowing in the earth and not caring about much else.

The Long-Nosed Mice hunted along this same riverbed. They, too, were persons of the early race. Unlike the Beetle, the Long-Nosed Mice were not so interested in earthy things. They could sniff with their long noses and detect things far away. This was useful when they went hunting.

The Beetle did not like the Long-Nosed Mice; they were persons too different from himself. So he thought of a way to kill them.

A Long-Nosed Mouse came hunting. The Beetle twirled a stick and said:

"Get out of the way,
The Beetle is throwing."

The Long-Nosed Mouse went where the Beetle was pointing to get out of the way. And the Beetle hurled his stick. It was a big stick and it made a sound in the air: "habbu, pu, pu, pu, pu, pu." The stick hit the Long-Nosed Mouse right on his face so he fell down and was dead.

The Beetle dragged the Mouse away.

Another Long-Nosed Mouse came hunting. The Beetle said:

"Get out of the way,
The Beetle is throwing."

The Long-Nosed Mouse went where the Beetle was pointing and he, too, was hit on the face, "habbu, pu, pu, pu, pu, pu." He was dead. The Beetle dragged him away.

This happened over and over again. Every Long-Nosed Mouse that came to the riverbed was killed.

Then one night Mantis dreamed about this. Early next morning he said that the Striped Mouse must go to the place where the Long-Nosed Mice had disappeared. The Striped Mouse must stop this killing of his friends, the Long-Nosed Mice.

Mantis told the wives of the Long-Nosed Mice that before the next day was over their husbands would come home. But they felt that their husbands were dead and they did not believe him.

81

The Striped Mouse as an animal has keen senses to guide him as he moves silently among bush and scrub and through his own secret tunnels. His nose is shorter than the exaggerated one of the Long-Nosed Mouse; it is more practical. The Striped Mouse as a person of early times was much like this.

He got up early the next day and went to the part of the riverbed where Mantis had said he would find the Beetle. The wife of the Striped Mouse sat up above the riverbed, sunning herself and keeping watch. She saw the Beetle coming and she said, "Oh my husband, come out! He is coming."

The Striped Mouse came out of a hole. Then the Beetle tried the same trick he had used on the Long-Nosed Mice. He said:

> *"Get out of the way,*
> *The Beetle is throwing."*

And he threw, "habbu, pu, pu, pu, pu, pu," hurling a big stick.

But the Striped Mouse did not go where the Beetle was pointing and he was not hit. He said, mocking the Beetle:

> *"The Beetle is throwing,*
> *Get out of the way."*

He picked up the stick and threw it back to the Beetle, "ket, te, te, te, te."

The Beetle said:

82

"Get out of the way,
The Beetle is throwing."

He threw the stick back again, "habbu, pu, pu, pu, pu."
Then the Striped Mouse said:

"Get out of the way,
The Beetle is throwing."

And he threw the stick, "ket, te, te, te, te." It knocked
the Beetle down and killed him.

Then the Long-Nosed Mice who had been killed by the
Beetle came to life again. They kept saying, "I am here, I
am here!" as they jumped up. They gathered together with
the Striped Mouse and his wife and they all went over the
hill and home. There the wives of the Long-Nosed Mice
were waiting, and Mantis said to them, "You would not
believe me, but I told you that what has happened would
happen—your husbands, the Long-Nosed Mice, are coming
home."

10 ✒ A Visit to the Lions

ONE DAY KWAMMANG-A SAID, "Oh, Mongoose, my son, let us go to visit the Lions; they will roast zebra meat for us."

Mongoose said, "We will do so."

Mantis said, "Let us do so."

"Oh, Mantis," Mongoose complained, "do sit down and stay here, for you will be afraid of the Lions."

"But I want to walk with you," Mantis said. "And I want to talk to my old friend the Lion."

So Mongoose consented, and they went.

They soon came across the Lions' tracks. Mongoose said, "Here are the Lions' tracks. They are carrying zebra meat."

They went on and reached the water where the Lions were resting. The Lions rose up. A little Lion said, "Kwammang-a is coming along there, and Mongoose comes with him."

86

Now Mantis really was afraid of the Lions. "Oh, Mongoose, put me into your bag!" he cried.

Mongoose stopped walking. "I wanted you to stay at home," he said. "I knew you would be afraid of the Lions."

Mantis begged, "Quickly put me in, Mongoose, quickly, so the Lions do not see me! Put me in feet first and let my head stick out. You must keep putting in meat for me to eat. I will look out with my eye."

Mongoose did as Mantis told him to do.

"Oh, Mongoose, you must put your cape over me," Mantis said.

Mongoose did so.

Then Mantis asked for an ostrich eggshell full of water. Mongoose put it by his head and Mantis drank.

Just then the little Lion came up. He caught sight of the strange shape in the bag. He sprang back crying because he heard Mantis whispering. Then he looked again and he saw Mantis's eye because Mantis kept peeping out from inside the bag. The little Lion cried out; he went crying to his mother. She soothed him and he was still.

"Oh, Mammy," he said, "take out for me the little hare in Mongoose's bag!"

He went again to look at Mantis. Mantis shut one eye and winked at him, whispering, "I would like to poke your eye out."

The little Lion again went crying to his mother. She was angry and she walked up stamping. She stood on Mantis, to crush him.

"Boo!" she said. "What is this making my child cry?"

Mantis was so frightened that he jumped out of the bag. He got feathers and flew up into the sky. Now Mantis often took with him a bag and a cape made of the skin of a hartebeest. At moments of great danger he could wrap the cape around him for safety. The bag and the cape, along with his quiver of arrows, his stick, and his sandals, could fly through the air by themselves when Mantis called them.

He called down to them now: "Oh, shoes, you must

come! Oh, hartebeest skin bag, you must come! Oh, quiver, come! Oh, cape, come!" They came flying through the air.

Mantis flew down into the water to renew himself. Then he came out and shook himself dry. He walked, for the water had washed away his feathers and he could no longer fly. He put on the cape, took up the quiver and bow, put on his shoes, and went home.

There he sat down and said to his wife, "Oh, Dassie, we went to visit the Lions and the Lion killed Kwammang-a. Another Lion swallowed Mongoose." In this way he lied to his wife, Dassie, because he was still afraid.

Then Dassie went out and saw Kwammang-a's party coming laden with zebra meat. She said to Mantis, "Is that not Kwammang-a coming there laden? You told a lie to me."

Mantis said, "I thought all the time that Kwammang-a would come carrying zebra meat."

89

Dassie said again, "You told a lie to me."

Kwammang-a walked up and unloaded the zebra meat. He was silent because he felt uncomfortable. Mongoose walked up to the hut and said, "Mantis was afraid of the Lions. He truly asked me to hide him in my bag." And he went on talking about Mantis.

Mantis was angry and ashamed. He lay down and hid his face.

11 🐛 Mantis Makes an Eland

O<small>F ALL THE ANIMALS</small>, Mantis loved best the eland and the hartebeest. One Bushman story says of them, "The Mantis loved them not a little, he loved them dearly, for he made his heart of the Eland and the Hartebeest."

The hartebeest is an antelope with a long neck and fine head, somewhat resembling the Mantis. As the Bushmen say, "It feels that it belongs to the Mantis; that is why its head resembles his head." This resemblance can be seen in some of the Bushman paintings on rocks.

Mantis loved the eland even more than the hartebeest. When Bushmen were asked where Mantis might be, they replied, "We do not know, but the Elands do. Have you not hunted and heard his cry, when the Elands suddenly

MANTIS MAKES AN ELAND

started and ran to his call? Where he is, Elands are in droves like cattle."

The greatest paintings, dances, music, and stories of the Bushmen are about the eland. Their hunters say that ever since the time of the first Bushman they have never killed an eland for meat without saying thank-you with a dance.

The eland is a noble animal, the greatest of the African antelopes. In the Bushman stories Mantis sometimes sits between the eland's horns, sometimes between its toes, the part of a living creature that feels the way as it walks upon the earth. Mantis seems to be showing that the way the eland walks through life is his way, also.

Like most Bushman stories, those about the eland vary according to the teller and the part of southern Africa from which they come. But in all of them the eland is a way to wisdom.

In the greatest of these stories Mantis himself makes an eland.

Mantis once picked up an old shoe that had been discarded by Kwammang-a, his son-in-law who was part of the rainbow. A shoe is an earthy thing, a covering for the foot that walks on the earth, and the Bushman shoe is a simple sandal made from an animal's skin.

Mantis took Kwammang-a's old shoe and put it in the water where the reeds grew and the birds sang. It was always in water that Mantis created new life.

He went away, then came back to look. An Eland was there, made from the old shoe, but it was still a tiny Eland and it needed the protection of the water that gave it life. So Mantis turned away.

Again he came, and this time he saw the small track of the Eland, where it had come out of the water and walked off to graze. Mantis rejoiced. This Eland was already strong enough to walk about on land.

Mantis waited, sitting by the water, and after a time the Eland came to drink. Mantis said to him, trilling his voice, "Kwammang-a's shoe piece!" And the Eland walked up to him and looked.

Mantis saw that this was still a young Eland and it needed help. He went to get some honey; honey would give wisdom to the young Eland.

Early the next morning, before the sun was up, Mantis came to the water with honey in a bag. The Eland was in the reeds. Mantis called to it: "Kwammang-a's shoe piece!" The Eland came out of the reeds and walked up to his father. His father took the honeycomb out of the bag and rubbed pieces of it all over the Eland's ribs, and splashed them, making them very nice.

The next day Mantis did the same thing. When he called, the Eland first stood shyly in the water, then he walked up to his father. He had grown. His father wept for joy as he rubbed his ribs again with honeycomb. Then he went away and the Eland went back to bask by the water.

94

For three days and three nights Mantis stayed away. He was testing the Eland, to see how it would grow by itself. The Eland grew as big and strong as a bull.

Then Mantis went out early. The sun rose as he came to the water. He called, and the Eland rose up and came to him. He was so mighty that the ground resounded as he came. Mantis sang for joy about the Eland:

Ah, a person is here!
Kwammang-a's shoe piece!
My eldest son's shoe piece!
Kwammang-a's shoe piece!
My eldest son's shoe piece!

And he rubbed the Eland with honey. Then he returned home. Next morning he took with him young Mongoose, his grandson. He told him to cover up his head, and Mongoose did so. When he uncovered his head he saw the Eland, and he exclaimed, "A person is yonder, standing yonder!"

Mantis said, "You think it is magic, but it is not. It is a small thing, a bit of your father's shoe." And they went home.

Mongoose told his father, Kwammang-a, about the Eland, and together they went to look at him when Mantis was not there. When he saw the Eland, Kwammang-a knocked it down and killed it for meat. He and Mongoose were cutting up the Eland, to eat it, and Mantis was not there.

When Mantis came and saw what they were doing he was angry and he said, "Why could you not first let me come?"

It was not the Eland's death that Mantis minded most. Death for Mantis was never the end, for he could re-create a new being from just a small part of the old. And he knew that animals must be killed for meat. What made him angry was that he had not been there. He scolded Kwam-mang-a because he had not let him be the one to kill the Eland.

Kwammang-a said to Mongoose, "Tell your grandfather to leave off! He must come and gather wood for us, that we may eat, for this is meat."

Mantis came, but he scolded and scolded, telling Kwam-mang-a again and again that they might have left the Eland to kill until he was there. Then his heart would have been comfortable. Now he was miserable because other people had killed the beautiful Eland whom he alone had made.

As Mantis went to gather wood he saw his Eland's gall on a bush where Kwammang-a had put it. Now the gall is the one part of an animal no Bushman would ever eat. It is a small bag containing a terribly bitter fluid. To Mantis it now seemed like a part of his own bitterness at what had happened. He told the gall he would jump on it.

And the gall said, "I will burst and cover you."

Young Mongoose then called over, "What are you looking at there? Where is the wood you are supposed to gather?"

So Mantis brought wood and put it down.

Then he went back to the gall and again told it he would jump on it.

And the gall said, "I will burst and cover you."

Young Mongoose scolded Mantis again: "Why do you keep going to that bush? You are not gathering wood. I know you, you are going to play tricks."

Kwammang-a saw what Mantis was doing and said to Mongoose, "We must make haste and go, for your grandfather has seen the Eland's gall. When he acts like this I know he is going to play tricks. Call your grandfather."

They put the meat into a net and prepared to go. But Mantis put one of his shoes in a bag of arrows he was carrying. On the way home he said that his shoe was missing, it must be lying where the Eland was cut up. He would have to fetch it.

Young Mongoose said, "We must go home, we really must go home."

And Mantis replied, "You can go home, but I must go and get the shoe."

Then Kwammang-a said, "Let your grandfather be! Let him turn back."

And young Mongoose said, "I do wish Mantis would for once listen when we speak."

97

Mantis said, "You always go on like this! I must really go and get the shoe."

Mantis turned back, ran up to the gall, and pierced it. It burst and covered his head. His eyes swelled up, he could not see. There was blackness everywhere, within him and without. All the bitterness of the world was his.

Mantis groped, feeling his way in the darkness. And as he went groping along, groping along, groping, his fingers touched an ostrich feather. He grasped it tight. This was a feather of the bird from whom, long, long ago, had come fire.

Mantis thought about that. He did not need the heat of the fire, but he needed light. Joyfully he threw the feather up into the sky, and he said to it, "You must now lie up in the sky; you must henceforth be the Moon. You shall shine at night. You shall by your shining lighten the darkness for men. . . . You are the Moon. . . . You fall away, you return to life again, you give light to all the people."

And so Mantis created the Moon and it was a light to all the people.

The moon lets the Bushmen know that light will come back into their lives even when they are so full of bitterness that they feel nothing but darkness within themselves.

12 ✒ Mantis and the Sheep

THE NEXT STORIES COME FROM a much later time than
the others. We know this because sheep appear in them,
and black men who own the sheep. The Bushmen, being
hunters, owned neither sheep nor cattle. Knowing the fate
of the Bushmen when the black people invaded their land,
we cannot be surprised that they considered them as blood-
thirsty as the ticks that clung to their sheep.

There is a grim feeling of doom in these stories. An
idyllic phase in the lives of Mantis and his family is about
to end. The Bushmen who invented the stories must have
felt that their pleasant way of life, too, would come to an
end as their enemies closed in, though they could not have
known what terrible slaughter was to come.

Mantis went to the black men's house. They saw him
coming and said to each other, "What man comes yonder?"

A black man said, "Mantis is coming yonder. We will

creep into the sheep's wool, like ticks, so he will not see us. This little child must stay and look after the pots on the fire. Old man Mantis will come up and question him and we will listen."

The black men hid themselves in the wool on the backs of the sheep. Mantis walked up to the child. "Do I look like a fighting man, that the people have gone away in fear? Only a black child is here, tasting this pot and sitting alone in the house."

The people listened in the sheep's wool. Mantis said, "I will lay down my quiver and eat this fat I have brought until I am satisfied. Then I will knock down this child, for he has no sense."

A black man fell down from a sheep's back. Mantis saw him and asked, "Where have you come from?"

The young man was silent. His sister fell down; his elder brother fell down and snatched the pot from the fire. Other men fell down at other fires, one by one.

A big young man slipped down beside Mantis and sat holding him by his cape. His brother slipped down on the other side of his cape. Another man sounded "vvvv" as he dropped down; he rustled.

An old man, their father, was still on a sheep's back. He said to another man, "You must wait, hold the stick ready to strike. We will knock Mantis down and the people be-low will beat him."

Mantis said to himself, "Let me move a little farther away."

He pulled at his cape but it was held fast to the ground. The old black man fell upon him and knocked him down. Another beat Mantis's shoulders with a stick. Black men sprang out on each side and beat Mantis all over until he screamed. He slipped out of his cape and the black men still beat him as he ran away.

As he ran he called to his hartebeest skin bag. His cape came, too, and his quiver, following him. Mantis got wings and went flying into the water. He swam across to the other bank, while his precious possessions followed.

"Wait for me over there," he told them. "I must come and pick you up slowly and carry you slowly, for I have been sorely beaten."

Mantis rested. Then he picked up all his things and went home.

Mongoose saw him and said, "Mantis comes slowly. The black men seem to have beaten him, as they are apt to do. They are angry people. He will not sleep well tonight."

Mantis sat down and said, "The people to whom I went were all hidden. They kept coming out from somewhere and they beat me, while the sheep were in their pen."

Mongoose scolded, "You went to the house to which people do not go when the sheep are in their pen. People merely look in passing and go on to their own homes. For those people are apt to beat a man to death because of the sheep."

Mantis agreed. "That is just what they tried to do. One man knocked me down, other people dropped down and struck me. Then I rose up and went into the water to wash off the blood, and my things followed me."

Mongoose complained, "You are sitting shivering because you went into cold water when you had wounds. You might have died without our knowing. You went to play tricks on those people whom you do not know. Nobody goes to them, because they are angry folk."

Mantis replied wearily, "Oh, Mongoose, you ought not to teach me now, for I am old. I feel as if I want to sit getting stories—those are what I want to hear. I will lie down, for my head aches. I really ache, I shall writhe in pain."

And he lay down to sleep and covered up his head.

Mantis lay moaning in his sleep. He dreamed that while the black men slept all their houses rose up, and their sheep, and they came and stood near Mantis's hut. The black people's capes came, too, and all their other things, even the sticks with which they had beaten Mantis.

Mantis kept on dreaming. When those people woke up, they would feel the cold. They would miss their houses, and their sheep. But they would not find any tracks, for the sheep had gone straight up in the air, and their pen with them. The black people would also miss the fire, and their cooking pots and their knives, for these had all gone, too.

The people would be walking about in the dark in their bare flesh because they could not find capes. They would sit in the cold because they had no houses. Without fire or knives these people would not be able to cook or roast meat to feed themselves. They would have to drink raw blood.

Mongoose woke up. Mantis said, "Oh, Mongoose, do you hear a bleating like sheep outside? It seems to have come while we were asleep."

Mongoose got up and went out and saw the sheep. He said, "Oh, people! Get up! Get up and look at the sheep which are in this pen which my grandfather Mantis has brought. The houses, too, and pots, and capes. Now I can keep warm from the cold. And here are the sticks with which they beat my grandfather. I shall keep them so that I can beat these people."

Mantis's wife, Dassie, got up.

"Oh, Mantis," she said, "why did you take away the people's sheep?"

Mantis answered, "It seemed right to me because those people attacked me, they wanted to kill me in their anger."

And he told about his dream, and about what he saw in the future: "In these pots the Bushmen will someday cook, because they will have fire. We ourselves will be different then. We will eat different things because we will not have fire. You, Mongoose, will then go to live in the hills with your mother. You will eat honey on the hill and you will marry a she-mongoose. Your mother will truly become a porcupine and live in a hole. Grandmother Dassie, the rock rabbit, will live in a mountain den. I, Mantis, will have wings. I will be a little green thing and I will fly."

Porcupine called to Kwammang-a, her husband. She used

his most intimate nickname because she was perplexed at what she saw. "Oh, Kwa! Look at the sheep Mantis has brought! We do not need to eat these up quickly, for the people do not know where they are, they did not see them go. The sheep went straight up in the air, with their pen, and came here. All the other things, too, while the people were sleeping."

Mongoose felt uneasy. He said, "Oh, Mantis! Now you should leave these people's things alone, that they may still have houses."

Mantis replied, "Do you not see why I thought it right to do this? These people did bad deeds to me, they wished me to tremble with the pain of my skin. I want them to see what I can do to them."

And so they prepared to eat the sheep.

13 ✏ The All-Devourer

THE ALL-DEVOURER IN THIS STORY seems much like the dragon of our fairy tales. He personifies both power and evil, yet he is also a member of the family. In real life the Bushmen were overcome by the enemies that beset them. In the story it is the Bushmen who conquer their dragon and go on to a new beginning.

Mantis had punished the black people by taking away everything they owned, but this did not make him happy. He still felt unwell. Something remained to be done before he could feel healed and he and all his family could get away from this disaster and start life over again.

Mantis told Mongoose to catch some fat sheep for his father, Kwammang-a, to cut up and hang up to dry. Kwam-mang-a could use the black people's own knives.

110

"I do not feel like cutting up," Mantis said. "I am still writhing with pain. When this swelling in my throat is over I can cut."

Young Mantis was there, and young Kwammang-a. But one person was missing from the family group. No one had asked the All-Devourer to come, the real father of Mantis's adopted daughter Porcupine. All people feared his ferocious ways, but now Mantis had decided that the family group must be complete. They must all eat the sheep together. Only then could they go on to better things.

Mantis said, "I want Porcupine to go out tomorrow and ask the Man yonder to come and eat these sheep with us, for they are plentiful."

Porcupine protested: "Do you really want me to go to my other father? A Man who devours things he is; he walks along eating up the bushes as he passes."

Mantis replied, "You must indeed go to your other father, the All-Devourer, that he may eat these sheep with us and drink this soup. I have poured away some of the soup because my heart is upset. I want the Old Man yonder to come. He will drink up the soup and then I can talk. Take cooked meat in a sack. Then he will not refuse to come."

"No one lives with that Man," Porcupine said, "because no one can hand him food. His tongue is like fire and he burns people's hands. The pots will be swallowed with the soup in them, and all the sheep in their pen. We will be swallowed with the sheep. Yonder Man behaves like this. He does not often travel because his stomach is so heavy. I,

111

Porcupine, am living with you because I am afraid my own father will devour me, and I know that you will not devour me." She sighed. "But I will fetch him tomorrow. Then you will see himself with your own eyes."

Porcupine went the next morning. She arrived at her father's, the All-Devourer's, and set down the sack of meat.

"Go!" she said. "Cousin yonder invites you to come and eat sheep with him, for his heart is troubling him. It is he who wants you to come. I have told you; now I will go on ahead."

She shook out the meat from the bag onto the bushes. The All-Devourer licked up the meat; he gulped down the bushes, too. Porcupine slung the bag over her shoulder and walked away quickly, in fear of the All-Devourer. She reached home before him.

Mantis asked her, "Where is Father?"

Porcupine answered, "He is still on the way. Look at that bush up there; watch for it to break off. Then the next bush. For his fiery tongue will take away the bushes before-hand, while he is still behind the hill. Then his body will come up and when he arrives all the bushes will be finished off. We will no longer sit hidden. Now I want Mongoose to eat plenty, for he will never get to eat those sheep. The Man yonder will swallow up the sheep."

The All-Devourer followed Porcupine's footsteps, eating bushes as he went. His shadow glided up to Mantis's hut. It fell upon Mantis.

Mantis looked at the sun. "Where are the clouds?" he

asked fearfully. "I do not see any clouds, but the sun is dark; it seems to be hidden by clouds."

Porcupine said to him, "There are no clouds. It is the Man's shadow. The shadow shuts us in altogether. When he reaches us the sun will seem to have set. I want Mongoose to hide this pot of food for me while there is still time."

Mantis saw the All-Devourer's tongue. He said to Porcupine, "I see a red fire yonder. Does your father hold fire in his hand?"

"It is the Man coming there," Porcupine answered. "His tongue is like fire. We will get out of the way. We will not hand him any food ourselves, but put something down for him, for his tongue would singe our hands. We do not hear the wind because he comes; it does not blow. He makes a shelter from the wind when he stands.

"He has put a layer of bushes at the bottom of his stomach, but he has not filled it up. He is still seeking food. If he finds none he will swallow all these people, for they invited him to come to food that was not enough.

"I want Dassie to hide the other pot, so she will still have soup."

The All-Devourer arrived. Mantis placed food for him. The All-Devourer gulped it quickly down. Mantis poured soup into a bucket. The All-Devourer swallowed the bucket. Mantis put meat into another bucket and pushed it towards the All-Devourer. The All-Devourer put out his tongue and scorched Mantis's hands.

Mantis took meat and put it in a cooking pot. He said to young Mantis, "Oh, child, make a good fire for this pot. I cannot do it for my hands are burning where Grandfather scorched me."

Young Mantis did so.

Mantis sat spitting on his hands to cool them. He ladled out another bucketful of meat and pushed it to the All-Devourer. The All-Devourer licked his hands. Mantis sprang back, lost his balance, and tumbled into the hut. He sat licking his hands and said to Mongoose, "Oh, Mongoose, give me meat to cook. The buckets seem to have vanished."

Mongoose scolded, "Mother told you it would be like this. You would not listen. You invited the big Cousin whom no one invites because his tongue is like fire."

Mantis called young Mantis, telling him to bring the meat Porcupine had hidden. "Look at the size of his stomach," he said.

He ladled up two more buckets and the All-Devourer gobbled them up. Mantis said, "Oh, Mongoose, quickly bring a sheep and cut it up."

The All-Devourer asked for water. Mantis set a whole water bag before him. The All-Devourer's tongue took up the bag and he swallowed it with the water in it.

"Oh, Mongoose," Mantis said, "fetch that water in the other water bag, for you see that this one has been swallowed. Grandfather turns his head, seeking more water. The sheep will soon be devoured."

The All-Devourer looked towards the sheep and he swallowed them all while they were still alive.

Porcupine winked at Mongoose to get his attention. "Oh, Mongoose!" she said. "Father will be swallowed if he goes on acting bravely like this. He will certainly be swallowed."

The All-Devourer called his name. He said to Mantis, "Oh, Mantis, bring out the things to which you invited me, the real things which I, a devourer of things, should eat."

He advanced; he burned Mantis with his tongue.

Mantis said, "I who am Mantis invited you who devour things to my home. You came and finished off my things. You should not ask for the real food. Those sheep that you devoured were the food; there is nothing else."

The All-Devourer sprang forward then and devoured Mantis. Young Mantis, his son, took up his bow and sprang away. Young Kwammang-a ran away. Mantis was quite silent because he was in the stomach.

The All-Devourer looked towards Kwammang-a and said that he was going to swallow him, his daughter's husband. He would do so, even though he was handsome. He quickly swallowed his daughter's husband and his stomach hung down almost to the earth.

Porcupine wept as her husband vanished into that vast stomach. She stood sighing. But then the children came from afar, and her courage returned. She asked young Mantis, "Are you a fierce man?" He was silent. She asked, "Are you angry?"

Young Mantis was silent because he did feel angry.

Porcupine also questioned her son, young Kwammang-a. She said, "Are you angry enough? You must remember that Grandfather's tongue is like fire. I do not want you to flinch."

Young Kwammang-a sat still because he was indeed angry. They agreed to cut his grandfather open.

Young Kwammang-a said to young Mantis, "You must cut one side of Grandfather while I cut the other. Then we must run away while our fathers pour out of his stomach."

The two children went in wrath to the All-Devourer. Silently they approached him as he lay in the sun. The All-Devourer stood up and waited. Young Mantis sat on the left of the All-Devourer because he cut with his left hand, like his father. Young Kwammang-a sat on the right side because he held his spear in his right hand.

The All-Devourer scorched young Mantis's temple with his tongue. He scorched the root of young Kwammang-a's ear, saying, "This little child really seems very angry."

He scorched one of young Mantis's ears, then the other. Young Mantis sat still.

Young Kwammang-a looked hard at young Mantis. He signaled him to hold his spear fast, and he held his own spear well. He sprang forward; he cut his grandfather's stomach. Young Mantis cut, too. Then they ran away.

The fathers poured out, the sheep also, the buckets, the pots, the bushes, all the things poured forth. The All-Devourer doubled up and died.

Young Mantis said, "Oh, bushes, we have cut you out! You will truly become bushes. You will grow as you did before. People can get dry bushes for their fire and warm themselves. These sheep will graze over the land again and return to their shelter. For that Man who ate up the bushes is utterly dead."

Mantis felt that his son's speech truly resembled his own. It was true.

Dassie gave Mantis water. She said to him, "Oh, Mantis, you must drink only a little!"

Mantis said, "I am dying of thirst. I must drink up the whole eggshellful."

He gulped the water and fell down. Dassie hit him on the shin with a stick until he got up. He sat there shivering while she held his face fast and rubbed it, helping him to be himself again.

She reproved him. "I told you to drink only a little water, but you would gulp it all down and nearly kill yourself."

Porcupine gave Kwammang-a water. "Oh, Kwammang-a!" she said, "you must drink only a little, just wet your mouth. And you must wash yourself, for you have just come out of the stomach in which you were. You can drink more when you feel warm."

Kwammang-a drank a little; he did not gulp it all down. Then he washed himself and drank some more. Porcupine cooked meat, for she had told Mongoose to hide some for her.

"We must first eat here," she said, "where the devouring Man lies dead. Then we will go far away, leaving him lying outside that hut. We will live in a different hut and that will be our home."

They all traveled away to a new home, leaving behind the Man who had devoured the people. There they made a new life for themselves and lived always in peace.

118

14 ✒ The Bushmen Today

AFTER THE SLAYING OF THE All-Devourer, Mantis and his family went away to find a place where they could make a new home and live in peace. In real life the Bushmen, slaughtered and hounded by their enemies, retreated to the peace of the desert. Between thirty and fifty thousand of them live in the Kalahari today. But even there they are not really safe. Though no one else wants to live on this land, no government has recognized the Bushmen's right to it.

A Bushman hunter may still be arrested and put in jail for killing an animal that is protected by law—though there is no other way he can live. His enemies may come and take him away, along with his women and children, to work for them. This is against the laws of every territory where the Bushmen roam, but laws of this kind are not strictly enforced in the desert. The Europeans still have guns and horses. The Bushmen dare not defend themselves with their poison arrows; no law protects them. And a Bushman who

is used to living in the wide vastness of the desert would often rather die than be shut up in the four small walls of a jail cell.

The Bushmen have no land. They ask the government, wherever it is, to "listen to the weeping of a race that is very tired of running away. Give us a piece of land, too . . . Bushman land."

What will happen next to the Bushmen?

It is hard for primitive people to preserve their way of life anywhere in the world today. The number of Bushmen is limited first of all by the difficult conditions under which they live. Then, when some are taken away to work for white people or black people, they lose contact with their former life. A few leave the desert willingly in time of drought to settle on farms where they are assured of food and water. Others have no choice but to leave when farmers encroach on the springs of sweet water on which their lives depend. Once they have left the desert, Bushmen often marry people of other races. The old ways are gradually forgotten.

Besides this, the arms of civilization reach farther and farther into the desert, wanting somehow to put these people to "good use." And "good use" means doing the kind of work that is considered important in our modern world: working on farms or in factories, mining gold, learning the ways of the white man. None of this belongs to the way of life of the Bushmen.

Why should we care, after all, what happens to the Bushmen of the desert? They earn no money and pay no taxes.

If they are left alone it is unlikely that they will ever become what we call "useful citizens."

True, but this is not the whole story.

Primitive people know that their very lives depend on wise use of nature. In our modern civilization of man-made gadgets and mechanical devices, we often forget that our lives, too, depend on the natural world around us. Yet the ancestors of the whole human race began in primitive wildness and were nourished by it for millions of years. At the very least, we might learn from the Bushmen something of our own early beginnings—something, too, of the power of nature to renew itself year after year, and to bring about a new beginning in the hearts of men.

Perhaps, after all, the people of southern Africa will let the Bushmen keep their way of life a little longer. All over Africa and elsewhere people are beginning to realize that much of the natural wildlife of the continent will soon vanish completely if it is not protected. In the Kalahari Desert itself such animals as the eland, the giraffe, the gemsbok, are protected by law. No one asks what use they are to society; it is recognized that the lives of people everywhere would be poorer without them. How can we say any less of the Bushmen, perhaps the oldest form of human life left on earth? And how can we deny them the right to live as they choose? They do no harm to anyone.

We can only hope that for many years to come the Bushmen will track across the desert in their own way, thinking their own thoughts, leaving their footprints in the sand, and "dreaming" their stories.

A Note on the Source of the Bushman Stories in This Book

Most of the stories in this book were collected by the German scholar Dr. Wilhelm H. I. Bleek, during the second half of the nineteenth century. Dr. Bleek settled in southern Africa in 1855. He first made an intensive study of other native languages, then turned to the language of the Bushmen who lived in the Cape Colony and Orange Free State.

The few pure Bushmen who remained were scattered throughout the most remote parts of the Kalahari Desert. As now, few white travelers crossed this desert. The harsh conditions of desert life did not tempt those few to remain long enough to find out much about the Bushmen. Besides, the Bushmen themselves generally avoided the white men.

Now and then, however, a desert Bushman would be caught killing a wild animal on a white man's land, or raiding a white man's flock of sheep or cattle. Though he may have killed only to keep himself and his family from starvation, if a Bushman was caught he was sent to prison.

Dr. Bleek obtained permission to take several of these Bushman prisoners to live in his home so that he could learn their language and write down their traditional stories. These Bushmen grew fond of Dr. Bleek; they told him much of the lore of their people.

One of the prisoners was an old man named Xhabbo, the Bushman word for dream. To Dream we owe much of what we know of Mantis, as well as the heartbreaking account of his longing for the stories of his people, which to him meant home.

The Bushman language includes many clicks and pops that seem strange to us. (A "lateral click" is something like the sound we might make to urge on a horse.) Dr. Bleek and his sister-in-law, Lucy C. Lloyd, worked out a system of printed signs to represent the Bushman sounds that could not be represented by the letters of our alphabet. The stories the Bushmen told to Dr. Bleek, and the accounts of their life with their people, were therefore written first in their own language, then translated into English. (The Cape Colony was ruled by the British and English was the official language.)

Dr. Bleek's work was scholarly and thorough. He took down what the Bushmen told him word for word. Even when some of the numerous repetitions were eliminated, this method did not make for easy reading. The stories in this book, though they have been kept as close as possible to the feeling and style of the original, have been simplified and partly rewritten.

We do not know how many of the stories collected by Dr. Bleek are still told among the Bushmen of the Kalahari Desert. Few of the Bushmen who lived in the Cape Colony survived the slaughter of their people. Those who remain do not often welcome white men to their dream world. But in any case we owe to Dr. Bleek the preservation of many remarkable stories told by the little people of the Kalahari.

⚓ Index

INDEX